BONY-LEGS

AND
OTHER STORIES

Compiled by Pat Edwards

Acknowledgements

Macmillan Publishing Co. USA for 'Bony-Legs' from *Bony Legs* text copyright © 1983 Joanna Cole, illustrations copyright Dirk Zimmer; William Heinemann Ltd, UK for 'A List' from *Frog and Toad Together* by Arnold Lobel; Simon & Schuster, for 'Another Mouse to Feed' from *Another Mouse to Feed* by Robert Kraus, illustrated by Jose Aruego and Ariane Dewey, text copyright © 1980 by Robert Kraus, illustrations © by Jose Aruego and Ariane Dewey. Pages 36-37 and 60-61 were written by Bill Boyle.

We are grateful to the following for permission to reproduce photographs: Barnaby's Picture Library p.60 above left (photo: O.J. Troisfontaines), p.60 below left (photo: Bill Coward), p.60 below right. OSF Picture Library p.45 (photo: Stephen Dalton).

Illustrators, other than those acknowledged with each story, include: Ian Forss pp.46–47; Linda Forss pp.48–49; Alan Marks pp.36–37, Marina Massiha pp.34–35; Barry Rowe pp.60–61; John Ward pp.32–33; Sue Yencken pp:62–64.

Contents

BONY-LEGS

Bony-Legs was a horrible, bad witch. She could run very fast on her bony old legs. Her teeth were made of iron, and she liked to eat little children.

She lived deep in the woods in a hut that stood on chicken feet. All day long she waited for children to pass by.

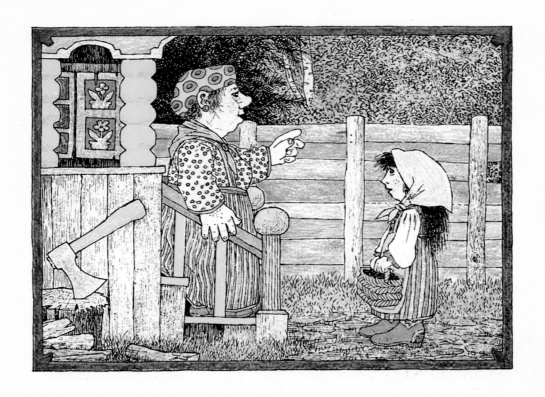

On the edge of the same woods a girl
named Sasha lived with her aunt. One
morning Sasha's aunt sent her out to
borrow a needle and thread. Sasha took
some bread and butter and a bit of meat
for lunch. She began to walk. She walked
and walked. She was surprised when she
came to a hut that stood on chicken feet.

She decided to go inside. She opened
the gate. It creaked and groaned. "Poor
gate," said Sasha. "You need some
grease." She scraped the butter from her
bread and rubbed it on the hinges of the
gate. It opened quietly. Sasha walked up
the path.

A skinny dog stood in her way. It barked and barked. "Poor dog," said Sasha. "You look hungry." She gave her bread to the dog. He ate it up and did not bark again.

A cat was sitting near the hut mewing sadly. "Poor kitty," said Sasha. "Are you hungry too?" She gave her meat to the cat.

Old Bony-Legs poked her head out the window.

"What do you want?" she asked Sasha.

"My aunt would like to borrow a needle and thread," said Sasha.

"Come right in," said the witch. Sasha went inside.

"Now," said Bony-Legs, "get into the tub."

"Why?" asked Sasha. "I don't need a bath."

"I want you nice and clean," said Bony-Legs. "I'm going to cook you for my supper."

She grinned and showed her iron teeth. Then she went outside to gather sticks for the fire. She locked the door behind her.

Sasha was scared. She began to cry.

"Don't cry," said a voice. "I will help you."

Sasha looked around. No one was there but the cat.

"Fill the tub but don't get in," said the cat. Sasha had never heard a cat talk, but she did what it told her.

Bony-Legs called through the door, "Are you washing, girl?"

"Yes, I am," said Sasha.

"Good," said Bony-Legs. And she went away to gather more sticks.

After she had gone the cat gave Sasha
a silver mirror.

"When you are in trouble, throw this
away," said the cat.

That does not make sense, thought
Sasha. But she took the mirror and put it
in her pocket.

"Now run," said the cat. Sasha climbed
out the window and began to run.

The witch called through the door again, "Are you washing, girl?"

"Yes, I am," said the cat.

"Well, hurry up," said Bony-Legs. Then she went away.

Sasha ran through the yard. The dog stopped her and gave her a wooden comb. "When you need help, throw this away," said the dog.

That does not make sense, thought Sasha. But she put the comb in her pocket.

Then she opened the gate. It did not make a sound on its buttered hinges. Sasha ran into the woods.

Bony-Legs called through the door
again, "Are you washing, girl?"

"Yes, I am," said the cat.

"What!" said Bony-Legs. "Not done yet?"

She flung open the door. There was the
cat. There was the tub. But where was
Sasha?

"You sneaky cat!" yelled Bony-Legs.
"Why did you trick me?"

"You never fed me," said the cat. "But
Sasha gave me meat to eat."

"Bah!" said Bony-Legs, and she ran into
the yard.

The dog was sleeping in the sun. "You
lazy dog!" shouted Bony-Legs. "Why
didn't you bark at her?"

"You never fed me," said the dog.
"But Sasha gave me bread to eat."

"Bah!" said the witch, and she rushed to the gate. "You worthless gate!" she screamed. "Why didn't you lock her in?"

"You never took care of me," said the gate. "But Sasha put butter on my hinges."

The old witch flew into a rage.
She stamped her feet, pulled her hair,
and even pinched her own nose. But she
did not feel any better.

She ran after Sasha on her bony old
legs. Sasha looked back and saw the
witch's iron teeth glinting in the sun.

Sasha was scared. She remembered
the silver mirror. She took it out of her
pocket and threw it behind her.

The mirror became
a deep, silver lake.
Bony-Legs could not
cross it.

She ran home and got her tub.

She rowed it across the lake

and ran after Sasha on her bony old legs.

Sasha saw the witch coming again.

She remembered the wooden comb.

She took it out of her pocket and
threw it behind her.

The comb grew
until it was as tall
as three trees.
Bony-Legs
could not climb
over it.

She could not dig under it.

She could not even squeeze through it.

At last she gave up. And she stamped her feet, pulled her hair, and pinched her nose all the way back to her hut.

Sasha went home, too. And you can be sure she never went back to the hut that stood on chicken feet. And for as long as she lived she never saw old Bony-Legs again.

story by *Joanna Cole*
pictures by *Dirk Zimmer*

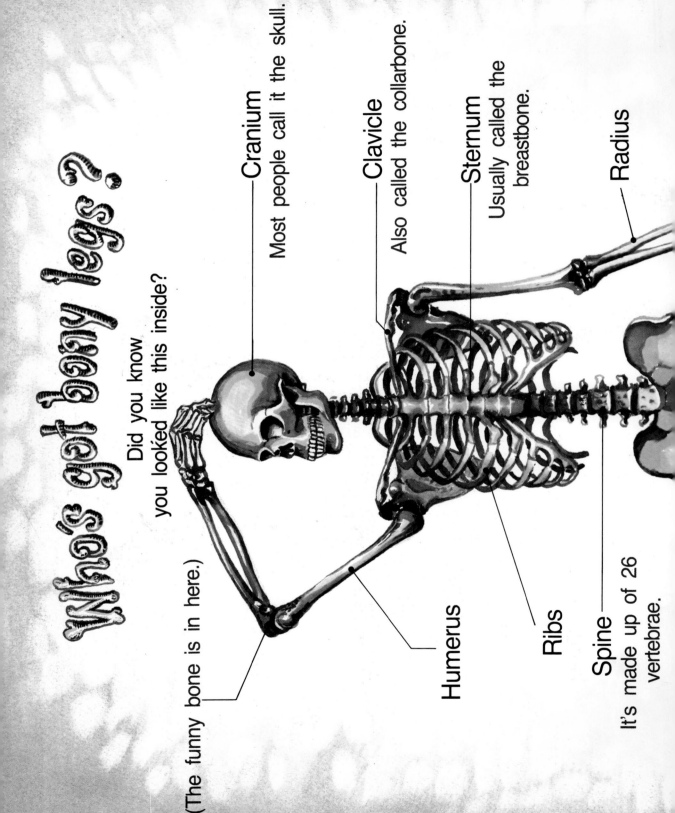

Who's got bony legs?

Did you know
you looked like this inside?

(The funny bone is in here.)

Cranium
Most people call it the skull.

Clavicle
Also called the collarbone.

Sternum
Usually called the breastbone.

Radius

Humerus

Ribs

Spine
It's made up of 26 vertebrae.

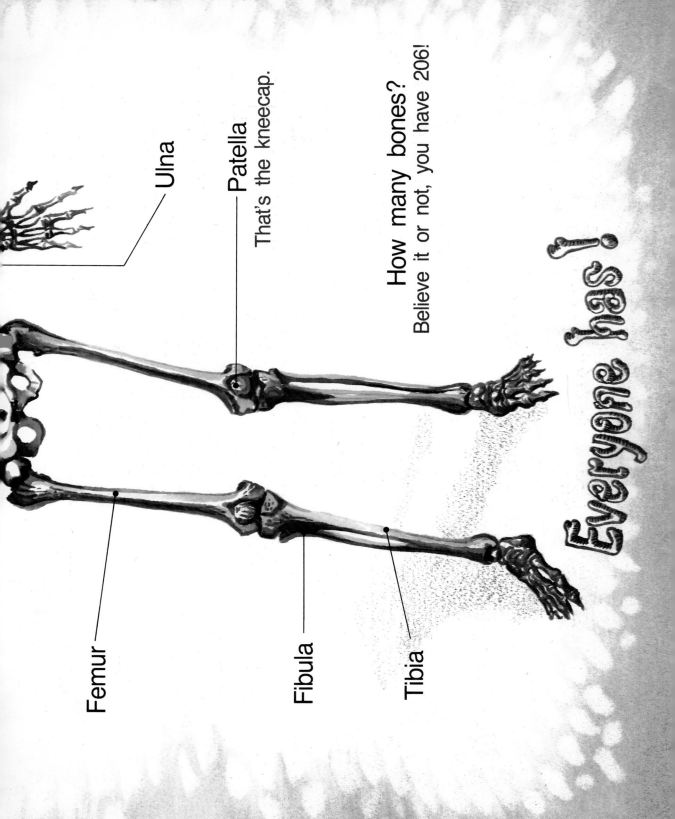

Ulna

Patella
That's the kneecap.

How many bones?
Believe it or not, you have 206!

Femur

Fibula

Tibia

Everyone has 1

Dry Bones

The toe-bone's connected to the foot-bone, the foot-bone's connected to the connected to the knee-bone, the knee-bone's connected to the thigh-bone, the back-bone, the back-bone's connected to the shoulder-bone, the

the ankle-bone's connected to the leg-bone, the leg-bone's connected to the hip-bone, the hip-bone's connected to the thigh-bone's connected to the neck-bone, the neck-bone's connected shoulder-bone's connected to the head-bone...

Hallowe'en

Special Days

Hallowe'en takes place each year on October 31st.
The word "hallow" comes from the Old English word
meaning holy. All-Hallow-Even, as it used to
be called, meant the night before
All Hallows – the Christian feast
of All Saints. On the day of
All Saints, the Church remembers
all who are saints.

In the old days, this
was a time of fear and
mystery. Stories of ghosts and witches,
evil spirits and spells terrified everyone. During
these times, October 31st was thought to be the last
day of the year. People believed that on this night the
evil spirits met. They carried out their wicked work in the
winter darkness. The tradition of wearing masks and lighting
lanterns began as a way of frightening off these spirits.

How do we celebrate Hallowe'en today?

Hallowe'en lanterns.
For Hallowe'en parties, the insides of turnips or swedes are hollowed out. Slits are cut for eyes, nose and mouth.
A lighted candle stands inside the lantern to make a spooky-looking face.

For hundreds of years, people took the witch on her broomstick very seriously. Today, witches and ghosts are just part of the Hallowe'en fun.

Apple games
Try to bite an apple, which can be either bobbing on a string or floating in a bowl of water.
The catch is – your hands are tied behind your back!

Apple games are linked to Hallowe'en from long ago. People collected apples and nuts in their winter store of food.

Trick or treat
Dressed like witches or ghosts, and carrying lanterns, children knock at neighbours' doors, saying, "Trick or treat". If they are not given sweets as a treat, they play a silly trick. But you should never play tricks which might hurt or frighten anyone.

A List

from
*Frog and Toad
Together*

One morning Toad sat in bed.

"I have many things to do," he said. "I will write them all down on a list so that I can remember them."

Toad wrote on a piece of paper:

A List of things to do today

Then he wrote:

Wake up

"I have done that," said Toad, and he crossed out:

~~Wake up~~

Then Toad wrote other things on the paper.

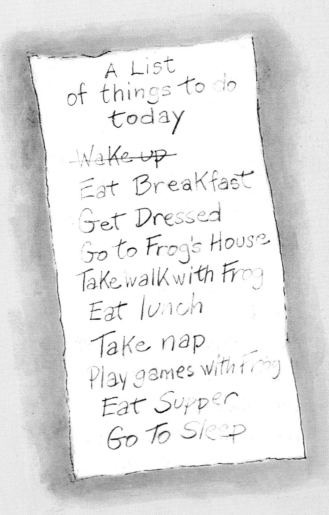

A List
of things to do
today

Wake up

Eat Breakfast
Get Dressed
Go to Frog's House
Take walk with Frog
Eat lunch
Take nap
Play games with Frog
Eat Supper
Go To Sleep

"There," said Toad.
"Now my day is all written down."

He got out of bed and had something to eat. Then Toad crossed out:

~~Eat Breakfast~~

Toad took his clothes out of the cupboard and put them on. Then he crossed out: ~~Get Dressed~~

Toad put the list in his pocket. He opened the door and walked out into the morning.

Soon Toad was at Frog's front door. He took the list from his pocket and crossed out: ~~Go to Frog's House~~

Toad knocked at the door.

"Hello," said Frog.

"Look at my list of things to do," said Toad.

"Oh," said Frog, "that is very nice."

Toad said, "My list tells me that we will go for a walk."

"All right," said Frog. "I am ready."

Frog and Toad went on a long walk.

Then Toad took the list from his pocket again. He crossed out:

~~Take walk with Frog~~

Just then there was a strong wind. It blew the list out of Toad's hand. The list blew high up into the air.

"Help!" cried Toad. "My list is blowing away. What will I do without my list?"

"Hurry!" said Frog. "We will run and catch it."

"No!" shouted Toad. "I cannot do that."

"Why not?" asked Frog.

"Because," wailed Toad, "running after my list is not one of the things that I wrote on my list of things to do!"

Frog ran after the list. He ran over hills and swamps, but the list blew on and on.

At last Frog came back to Toad.

"I am sorry," gasped Frog, "but I could not catch your list."

"Blah," said Toad.

"I cannot remember any of the things that were on my list of things to do. I will just have to sit here and do nothing," said Toad.

Frog sat with him. Toad sat and did nothing.

After a long time Frog said, "Toad, it is getting dark. We should be going to sleep now."

"Go to sleep!" shouted Toad. "That was the last thing on my list!"

Toad wrote on the ground with a stick: Go to sleep

Then he crossed out:

~~Go to sleep~~

"There," said Toad. "Now my day is all crossed out!"

"I am glad," said Frog. Then Frog and Toad went to sleep.

by *Arnold Lobel*

Fantastic Frog

A Leopard Frog

RULES FOR TOTAL FRIENDSHIP

Your attention, please!

$1 + 1 = 2$

FROG + TOAD = TOADAL FROGSHIP

total   friendship

BECAUSE....

1. Frog and Toad love to do things together, like leaving footprints in the mud.

2. Frog and Toad show they care for each other by sharing.

3. Frog is glad when Toad is happy, and Toad is glad when Frog is happy.

4. Frog and Toad always listen to each other and help each other out of jams.

Another Mouse to Feed

Mr and Mrs Mouse had many children, so many in fact that they often forgot their names, as well as how many they had.

To help make ends meet, Mrs Mouse got a job as a roller skating instructor. It was a lot of work, but she never complained because she loved little mice, especially her own.

It was a lot of work for Mr Mouse too. In fact, he had to have three jobs to earn enough money to take care of his family, but he didn't mind, because he too loved little mice, especially his own.

"I have my hands full with all these mice," said Mrs Mouse. "I think our family is big enough."

"I don't think I could manage four jobs," said Mr Mouse. "I think our family is big enough, too."

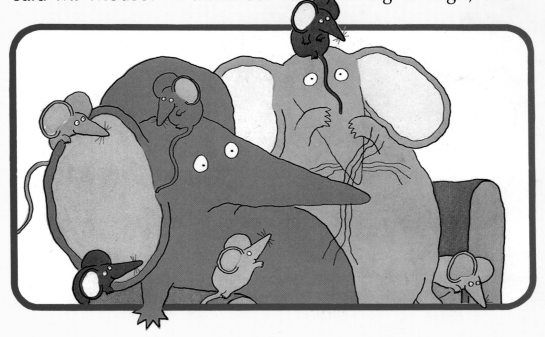

They were just having a cup of tea, when there was a knock on the door.

"Who could it be at this time of night?" asked Mrs Mouse.

"There's one way to find out," said Mr Mouse, and he opened the door. And on the doorstep was a wicker basket containing a tiny mouse, wrapped in a blanket. A note was pinned to the blanket, reading: "Take care of my child."

"A mouse in need . . ." said Mrs Mouse, "is another mouse to feed," said Mr Mouse.

All the mouse children were delighted. It was nice to meet a mouse who wasn't a brother or a sister.

Mrs Mouse went to the employment agency to get a second job.

At home, Mr Mouse started scrubbing clean clothes and stirring empty pots.

They were both cracking up.

Edgar, the oldest child, noticed it first, and he told the others.

"If two parents can support thirty-one children, then thirty-two children can support two parents," Edgar declared. "Dad, you take a much-needed holiday from your jobs. Mum, you forget about teaching roller skating for now. Your children are going to take over."

"But what about your education?" asked Mrs Mouse.

"We'll work after school, weekends and holidays," said Edgar.

So all the mouse children who were old enough got after-school jobs,

and those who weren't old enough to go to school, did housework and took care of the new mouse.

Edgar, modelling himself after his father, got two after-school jobs: delivering newspapers and sweeping up in a grocery store.

And with seventeen mice cleaning house, it was spotless; with fourteen mice working, the money was soon rolling in.

Edgar kept it in sweet jars. He spent what was needed for necessities and saved what was left for a rainy day.

Soon, Mr Mouse and Mrs Mouse were rested and eager to get back to work. "I'd go nuts just sitting around," said Mr Mouse.

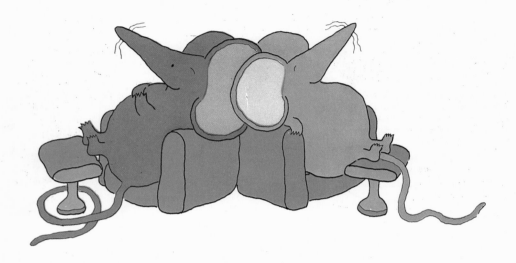

Mr Mouse became a fireman

and Mrs Mouse became
a tennis instructor.

Mr and Mrs Mouse also began scrubbing, cleaning and
cooking again.

But sometimes they just sat down and enjoyed their children.

58

All the mouse children continued their after-school jobs because they enjoyed working, and the extra money helped.

Before long, Baby Mouse was helping, too.

story by *Robert Kraus*, pictures by *Jose Aruego and Ariane Dewey*

It's my home

London

Welcome to the capital of the United Kingdom. London is the twelfth largest city in the world and there are about seven million people living here.

The Tower of London is where I work. I'm one of the Yeoman Warders who guard the Crown Jewels which are on show here.

The legend says that if I leave the Tower, it will fall, so my wings are clipped!

The Houses of Parliament stand alongside the River Thames. The Members of Parliament who make up the government rule the country from here.

Buckingham Palace is the London home of the Queen. If the flag is flying, it means that she is at home.

The River Thames

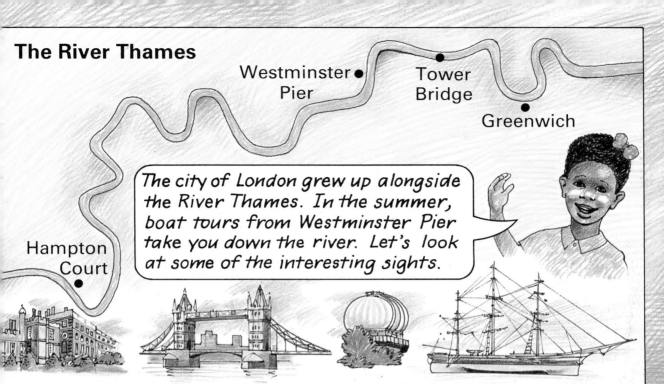

Westminster Pier

Tower Bridge

Greenwich

Hampton Court

The city of London grew up alongside the River Thames. In the summer, boat tours from Westminster Pier take you down the river. Let's look at some of the interesting sights.

Hampton Court Palace was built in 1515. Don't get lost in the Great Maze.

Tower Bridge was built in 1894 and opens to let big ships through.

At Greenwich you can visit the old Royal Observatory and climb aboard the Cutty Sark – an old clipper ship which was used for carrying tea.

Sightseeing in London

Don't miss these famous sights.

Post Office Tower

The Science Museum

The Monument

Regent's Park Zoo

Madame Tussaud's

Piccadilly Circus

St Paul's Cathedral

Westminster Abbey

Rules for living together successfully...

1 It's important to pull your weight . . .

2 Remember: many paws make light work . . .

3 Don't get cheesed off! It won't help . . .

4 Think about the needs of others . . .

False friends are like
autumn leaves
Found everywhere.
True friends are like
diamonds
Precious and rare.

Anon

What goes snap, crackle and squeak?

Mice Krispies!

Helpful words for mice and children

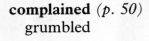

Glossary

complained *(p. 50)*
grumbled

creaked *(p. 6)*
made a loud, squeaking sound

delighted *(p. 53)*
very pleased about something

employment agency *(p. 53)*
a place you go to when you
want to get a job

hinges *(p. 6)*
the pieces of metal that help
a gate or door to swing open

mewing *(p. 8)*
meowing

gather *(p. 11)*
to collect together

glinting *(p. 20)*
sparkling or gleaming

grease *(p. 6)*
an oil that makes hinges
work smoothly

necessities *(p. 55)*
important things like
food and clothing

pesky *(p. 47)*
annoying; causing
trouble

worthless *(p. 18)*
no good at all

64